Rumpelst

Retold by Annette Smith
Illustrated by Pat Reynolds

NELSON PRICE MILBURN

Once upon a time,
there was a miller
who was always boasting
about his beautiful daughter.

"She is clever, too,"
he told everyone he met.
"My daughter is so clever,
she can spin straw into gold."

The King heard about the miller's boast.

"Spin straw into gold!
Bring that girl here!"
he commanded.
"If the miller has lied,
I shall throw his daughter
into prison."

3

The miller's daughter trembled with fear
as she stood before the King.
"I cannot spin straw into gold,"
she said to herself.

The King led her to a room
filled with straw.
In the room was a spinning wheel.

"This is the finest straw
in my kingdom," said the King.
"You must spin all of it
into gold by morning."

With that, he strode out of the room
and locked the door.

The miller's daughter was terrified.
"What am I to do?" she sobbed.

Suddenly, a strange little man
climbed in through the tiny window.

"I will spin this straw into gold," he said.
"But what will you give me in return?"

"You can have my necklace,"
said the miller's daughter.

"Well, I suppose it will have to do,"
muttered the strange little man,
and he set to work at once.

Whirr! Whirr! Whirr!
went the spinning wheel.

Soon the room was filled
with the finest golden thread.
When the last piece of straw
had been spun into gold,
the strange little man disappeared.

In the morning,
the King was amazed
to see so much gold.

But he was a greedy King.

He led the miller's daughter
to another room filled with straw.
This room was even bigger
than the first room.

"You are to spin all of this straw into gold by morning," he commanded, locking the door behind him.

The miller's daughter sobbed and sobbed.

All at once, the strange little man appeared again.

"If I spin all of this straw into gold," he said, "what will you give me?"

"My ring," said the miller's daughter. "You can have my ring."

The strange little man took the ring and began to spin the straw into gold.

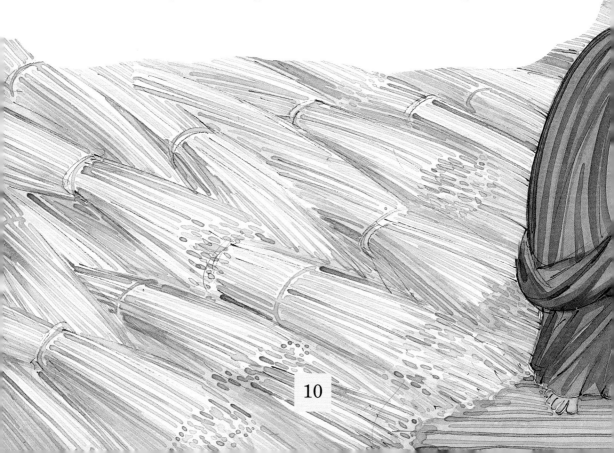

Whirr!   Whirr!   Whirr!
went the spinning wheel.
Whirr!   Whirr!   Whirr!

The strange little man worked all night,
then disappeared once more.

In the morning, the King was delighted
to see this room glittering with gold, too.
And he led the miller's daughter
to yet another room.

This room was even bigger than the others,
and it was filled with straw
from top to bottom.

"If you spin all of this straw
into gold by morning," he said,
"I will make you my wife."

The King was beginning to think
that the miller's daughter
was clever as well as beautiful.
He was becoming very rich.

As he locked the door,
the miller's daughter
sobbed and sobbed and sobbed.

13

Once again, the strange little man appeared.

"I have nothing left to give you," wept the miller's daughter.

"You will marry the King," said the strange little man, "and you will have a baby. If I spin all of this straw into gold, you must promise to give me the baby in return."

The miller's daughter gave her promise. There was nothing else she could do.

Whirr!   Whirr!   Whirr!
went the spinning wheel.
Whirr!   Whirr!   Whirr!
Whirr!   Whirr!   Whirr!

Once more, the room was filled with gold.
And so, the King married
the miller's daughter.

A year passed, and the miller's daughter,
who was now the Queen, had a baby boy.

One day, the strange little man
appeared again.
"I have come for the baby," he said.

The Queen held the baby tightly.
She had forgotten her promise.

"No! No!" she cried.
"You can have all the jewels
and gold in the kingdom,
but you cannot have my baby."

She began to sob.

The strange little man felt sorry for her.
"I will give you three days
to tell me my name," he said.
"Each day, you can have three guesses.
If you have not guessed my name
after three days, the baby will be mine."

The Queen sent messengers all over the land in search of names.

When the strange little man appeared on the first day, the Queen asked him, "Is your name Jack, or John, or Ivan?"

"No. Those names are not mine," grinned the strange little man.

The next day, the Queen asked, "Is your name Longbeard, or Skinny Legs, or Big Foot?"

"No! Those names are not mine, either!" laughed the strange little man.

By now, the Queen was very worried.

Late that night, a messenger returned to the castle.

He had something to tell the Queen.

"This evening as I was riding
through the forest,
I saw a strange little man.
He was dancing round the fire singing,

*Rumpelstiltskin is my name so fine,
Tomorrow the baby will be mine!* "

When the strange little man appeared
on the third day, the Queen said,
"Is your name Flip Flop or Nick Nack?"

"No! No!" he chortled.

"Then your name must be Rumpelstiltskin!"
said the Queen.

When the strange little man
heard his name, he flew into a rage
and stamped out of the palace,
never to be seen again.

A play

Rumpelstiltskin

People in the play

 Reader

 Miller's Daughter/ Queen

 Miller

 Strange Little Man

 King

 Messenger

Reader

Once upon a time, there was a miller
who was always boasting
about his beautiful daughter.

Miller

My daughter is very beautiful
and she is clever, too.
She can spin straw into gold.

Reader

A messenger for the King heard
the miller's boast and he rode back
to the palace to tell the King.

King

Spin straw into gold!
Bring that girl here to me.
If the miller is lying,
then I shall throw his daughter into prison.

Reader

The miller's daughter trembled with fear
as she stood before the King.

Miller's Daughter (to herself)

I cannot spin straw into gold.
Oh, why did my father
have to be so boastful?

King

Come with me, girl. We shall see
if you can spin straw into gold.

Reader

The King led the miller's daughter
to a room filled with straw.
In the room was a spinning wheel.

King

This is the finest straw in my kingdom.
You must spin all of it
into gold by morning.

Reader

The King strode out of the room
and locked the door.

Miller's Daughter (sobbing)

Oh, what am I to do?

Reader

Suddenly, a strange little man appeared.

Strange Little Man

I will spin this straw into gold.
But what will you give me in return?

Miller's Daughter

Here, you can have my necklace.

Strange Little Man

Well, I suppose it will have to do.

Reader

He set to work at once,
and soon the room was filled
with the finest golden thread.

Miller's Daughter
Thank you!   Thank you!

Reader
The strange little man disappeared
as quickly as he had appeared.
In the morning, the King was amazed
to see so much gold.

King
It is true!   You can spin straw into gold.
You have done well, girl.

Reader
But the King was a greedy man.
He led the miller's daughter
to an even bigger room filled with straw.

King
You are to spin all of this straw
into gold by morning,
or I will throw you into prison.

Miller's Daughter (sobbing and sobbing)
Oh, what am I to do?
There is even more straw in this room.

Reader
All at once, the strange little man
appeared again.

Strange Little Man
If I spin all of this straw into gold,
what will you give me?

Miller's Daughter
You can have my ring.

Reader
The strange little man took the ring
and began to spin the straw.
Whirr! Whirr! Whirr!
The strange little man worked all night,
then he disappeared once more.

Reader

In the morning, the King was delighted
to see this room also glittering with gold,
and he led her to yet another room.

King

This room is much bigger than the others.
If you spin all of his straw into gold
by morning, I will make you my wife.

Reader

The King was beginning to think
that the miller's daughter **was** clever
as well as beautiful. He left the room
and locked the door behind him.

Miller's Daughter (sobbing and sobbing)

If only the strange little man
could help me one more time.

Reader

The strange little man appeared again.

Strange Little Man

What will you give me this time?

Miller's Daughter (sobbing)

I have nothing left to give you.

Strange Little Man

You will marry the King
and you will have a baby.
If I spin all of this straw into gold,
you must promise to give me
the baby in return.

Miller's Daughter

I promise. I will do as you say.

Reader

Once more, the strange little man
sat down at the spinning wheel.
By morning, this room was filled
with gold, too.

Reader

A year passed, and the miller's daughter,
who was now the Queen, had a baby boy.
One day, the strange little man
appeared again.

Strange Little Man

I have come for the baby.
You gave me your promise.

Queen (sobbing)

No! No! You can have all the jewels
and gold in the kingdom,
but you cannot have my baby.

Strange Little Man (feeling sorry for her)

I will give you three days
to tell me my name.
Each day, you can have three guesses.
If you have not guessed my name
after three days, the baby will be mine.

Reader

The Queen sent messengers all over
the land in search of names.
When the strange little man appeared,
the Queen had three names to ask him.

Queen

Is your name Jack, or is it John?

Strange Little Man (laughing)

No! No! Those names are not mine.

Queen

Is your name Ivan?

Strange Little Man

No! That is not my name, either.

Reader

The strange little man danced with glee
and disappeared out of the palace.
The next day, the Queen had
three more names to ask him.

Queen
Is your name Longbeard,
or Skinny Legs, or Big Foot?

Strange Little Man
No! No! No!
Those names are not mine, either.

Reader
By now, the Queen was very worried.
Late that night, a messenger
returned to the castle.
He had something to tell the Queen.

Messenger
This evening as I was riding
through the forest,
I saw a strange little man
dancing around a fire singing,
Rumpelstiltskin is my name so fine,
Tomorrow the baby will be mine!

Reader

When the strange little man
appeared on the third day,
the Queen said to him:

Queen

Is your name Flip Flop, or Nick Nack?

Strange Little Man (chortling)

No! No!

Queen

Then your name must be Rumpelstiltskin!

Strange Little Man (stamping his foot)

Who told you my name?
Who told you my name?

Reader

The strange little man was so angry
that he stamped out of the palace
and was never seen again.